We love Alex and Hannah. So much pr
about walking with God and experier
love this series.

> *Dr. Kwesi Kamau, Lead Pastor, IMPACT Church, Dallas TX*

The Naturally Supernatural Course helped me live with a different awareness of
God's supernatural activity and equipped me with practical tools that help me
live more open to the supernatural work God wants to do in and through me.
Alex and Hannah are great teachers (and fun)!

> *Tammy Melchien, Teaching Team Pastor, Community Christian Church,
> Chicago IL*

The question that has dominated my thinking this last year is, 'What would it
look like to let Jesus lead Jesus' church?' A large part of that answer has to be that
Jesus' leaders need to know his voice. Alex and Hannah's approach to topics
such as Hearing the Voice of God has been for me tremendously helpful, biblical
and out right exciting. I could not commend them more strongly.

> *Chuck Gschwend, Founder of Renewal Coaching, AR*

The Naturally Supernatural Course encouraged, challenged, and fed me spiritually, and God has used these times to deepen my relationship with the Holy
Spirit. My view of God and my desire for Him has been enlarged through Alex
and Hannah's leadership, and I have been equipped to lead our church through
multiple series on the Spirit and His gifts.

> *Marshall Benbow, Lead Pastor, Grace Community Church, Greensboro NC*

The Naturally Supernatural materials have been a great help in our personal dis-
cipleship and as we lead others. We have found ourselves being more attentive
to the Holy Spirit's voice, more bold in asking for healing prayers and miracles.
And God has been so faithful to answer!! These materials helped jump start
us into a new season of being 'the Church' and participating in bringing God's
kingdom where we live, work and play.

> *Steve and Cindy Shogren, Wellspring Ministries, Mount Pleasant UT*

"I want to know Christ and the power of his resurrection and the sharing of his sufferings by becoming like him in his death" (Philippians 3:10). When meditating on this verse, I realized that I understood suffering but that I hadn't experienced much resurrection power in my spiritual life. God led me to the Absaloms' course, and coming from a church background that did not emphasize living supernaturally, I can say that I was not 'weirded out'! It really is natural. I took what I learned back to my church and we started developing the gift of prophecy (and we received words from God), prayer for healing (and we saw people healed), deliverance (and we saw people delivered), etc. This course helped to strengthen myself and my church in an area of weakness.

Jayme Himmelwright, Columbia SC

The Naturally Supernatural training was a true catalyst for my spiritual life. I did everything that Alex and Hannah taught and for the first time in my life I saw people get healed, I've shared prophetic words (that were accurate), and I've seen people freed from spiritual oppression. I highly recommend it.

Josh Wagner. Pastor. Indianapolis IN

I endorse this teaching with my whole heart. Gleaning from the expertise and experience that Alex and Hannah offer has greatly enhanced my ministry to others.

Bonnie C. Wetzel, MSW, LCSW, Raleigh NC

Alex and Hannah are a great team together. As someone who appreciates practical learning and application, we thoroughly enjoyed learning more about spiritual gifts taught in a very practical way. They gave us homework assignments to practically practice what we learned.

Jeremy and Andrea Harper, church planters, Columbus OH

Naturally Supernatural has been an incredible tool to come across. Straightforward, easy to understand, and biblically sound, the Absaloms have provided a resource that is imperative to our faith journey today. I highly recommend this course for churches and individuals alike.

Janine Koller, Prayer Director, Yakima WA

I've listened to God's voice for years, but the Naturally Supernatural Course has given me a biblical foundation that helps me understand and apply my prayer/prophetic experiences. I highly recommend this course to anyone who would like to grow in their ability to hear God's voice, or help others do so as well.

Emily Brown, Saugatuck MI

This course was incredibly helpful. All material was thoughtfully anchored in the Bible, and tremendously practical even for beginners looking to start ministering in the power of the Spirit. Alex and Hannah are humble, grounded, and eager to serve the church. Highly recommended!

John McHale, Mosaic Church of Richardson TX

The Naturally Supernatural Course helped me to start dialoguing with the Lord Jesus daily - not only praying, but asking Him and listening to Him. The Course changed my life!

Alena Vrlikova, Slovakia

The Naturally Supernatural Course has been wonderful for my growth in intimacy and partnership with the third person of the Trinity. It challenged my understanding of Scripture and has given me a great Kingdom framework to move out with the Spirit in proclaiming and demonstrating the power of the Gospel.

Lee Simmons, Pastor, Greensboro NC

The Naturally Supernatural Course was incredibly helpful! Alex and Hannah are thoughtful and encouraging guides that will help you hear the voice of God. Deeply theological and yet pragmatic and accessible! I wish I had found this course years ago!

Chris Brister, Lead Pastor, Union Church, Auburn AL

This material has truly been life changing for me - both personally and in ministry. It is full of biblical wisdom as well as practical steps to live a naturally supernatural life. I highly recommend this course!

Rachel Waldron, Destiny Church, Leesburg VA

THE

naturally

S U P E R N A T U R A L

C O U R S E

COURSE BOOK B: WARFARE

Alex and Hannah Absalom

The Naturally Supernatural Course - Course Book B: Warfare

Copyright © 2022 Alex and Hannah Absalom

Published by Dandelion Resourcing, Edmond, OK - dandelionresourcing.com

To contact Alex and Hannah about speaking at your conference or church, please visit dandelionresourcing.com

Design and Layout: Caity Shinnick

ISBN: 978-1-951420-05-5

With deepest gratitude to the many who have shown us — publicly and privately,
in person and in print — how to practice a naturally supernatural lifestyle.

CONTENTS

INTRODUCTION

Welcome to the Naturally Supernatural Course Book!

THE AIM OF THIS COURSE

The Naturally Supernatural Course is designed to help you discover how God has wired you to live a Spirit-empowered lifestyle.

As disciples of Jesus, we are given access to heavenly authority and power to play our part in extending His kingly rule. This is an empowering to build up the body of Christ in both depth and number.

However, so many believers don't know how to do this in practice. Whether it's a lack of healthy modeling, or few simple and repeatable practices, or the absence of clear Biblical undergirdings, or it simply slipping off our radar, the reality is that many of us struggle to healthily exercise a range of the naturally supernatural gifts of the Spirit.

This course is designed to help you:

- **UNCOVER** how to step more into the power and gifts of the Holy Spirit with the Naturally Supernatural Course.

- **BECOME** a biblically grounded practitioner of the more supernatural works of the Spirit.

- **EXPERIENCE** living by expectant faith while modeling pastoral kindness and love.

By God's grace, this is what lies in store for you now!

THE POWER OF COMMUNITY LEARNING

Most people will be watching these videos and doing the homework as part of a group of believers. While you can use this material by yourself - it will certainly still make sense and can be deeply applied - you will gain even more by buddying up with a few others from your church or ministry and working through it together. That way, you will learn from their stories and insights (as they will from you!), and there will be local accountability for following through on what you commit!

As you step into this resource, you'll see that there is plenty of space for you to write notes, add comments, ask questions, and discuss things with others in your local context. Remember that this is less about coming up with the 'right' set of answers, and more about allowing the Spirit to shape you through what you learn from the Bible, the teachings, your conversations, and your attempts to put things into practice in your everyday life.

OVERVIEW OF THE WHOLE COURSE

The whole course is divided into four parts, in order to give you bite sized chunks (the total 24 sessions could sound a bit intimidating!)

You have in your hands the Course Book for Part B: Warfare.

To help you see how this fits within the whole Naturally Supernatural Course, here's the Course overview:

PART A — FOUNDATIONS

MODULE A1: HEARING THE VOICE OF GOD
Session 1 - Prophecy Foundations
Session 2 - Prophecy Processing

MODULE A2: HEALING THE SICK
Session 1 - How to Minister Healing
Session 2 - Healing and Faith

MODULE A3: NATURALLY SUPERNATURAL THEOLOGY
Session 1 - The Naturally Supernatural Kingdom
Session 2 - Living in the Tension of the Now and the Not Yet

PART B — WARFARE

MODULE B1: BEING FILLED WITH THE HOLY SPIRIT
Session 1 - How to Be Filled With the Holy Spirit
Session 2 - The Gift of Tongues

HOW TO USE THE MATERIAL

1. WHAT HAPPENS

Within each session you will receive teaching totaling around 40 minutes, broken up into chunks. At regular intervals you will be asked to pause the video to answer an application question, engage with a self-assessment, or sometimes even try an activation exercise.

Each session will end with homework being set, followed by a discussion time in your local group. You'll see that we provide lists of questions in your Course Book to help that along, although feel free to ignore those and come up with your own better conversation starters!

If you perhaps miss your session and are catching up later on, or if you are going through the Course by yourself, we suggest you write down your responses in this Course Book. That will help you frame your thoughts more clearly (as would happen in a conversation), and will build clearer action steps for you to live out.

Finally, if you haven't yet purchased access to the videos, or you haven't yet created your own account as part of your church's pass, then please go to naturallysupernaturalcourse.com.

2. HOMEWORK

As you have seen from the Course overview, each Module has two sessions within it. We've designed it this way because that creates time and space for you to ponder that topic over the following days, coming back to the second session with reflections and questions.

To help this process along, at the end of every session we give you homework!!

Don't freak out, though, if you don't think of yourself as particularly academic. The homework will always be practical. It is intended to help you live differently, so you'll find it's not about hitting the books or doing memorization, but rather immersing yourself into a new (or renewed) skill set.

Sometimes you will find the homework to be very stretching - which is on purpose! For instance, when you are in the module on healing the sick, one homework is to pray for at least four different people for healing between the sessions. While obviously there's nothing special about the number four, the point is that we want you to try ministering healing on multiple occasions, so that you gain a range of experiences. If we just said, 'try once', then everything would hang or fall on how well that one attempt went down!

Don't worry if you 'fail' or struggle with the homework. As long as you process and then grow, you will perhaps learn even more from those tough moments. Don't forget, the goal here is living out what you are discovering about the Spirit's empowering presence in and through you.

So please embrace the homework exercises. They're actually a lot of fun, and we're sure that as your group recounts their experiences, you will laugh, ponder, and be stretched in your own faith.

MODULE B1:

Being Filled with the Holy Spirit

SESSION 1:

HOW TO BE FILLED WITH THE HOLY SPIRIT

HOMEWORK REVIEW

(If you haven't previously done Part A: Foundations, then skip this homework review. Otherwise, please take the time to review how things have gone since then!)

Are you someone who has to overcome cessationist theology or thinking?

What are the three things that you'll be doing to lean more into the 'Now' over the 'Not yet' of the Kingdom?

"The greatest need today is for men and women who k now Jesus Christ

as Savior to be filled with the Holy Spirit. If we are not filled with the

Holy Spirit, we are sinning against God."

Billy Graham

Probably we are all a bit heretical on this topic, so come with humility!

REFLECTION

As you hear about being filled with the Spirit, on a scale of 1 to 5 (where 5 = highly), how open do you feel to this topic and experience?

Circle your answer.

1   2   3   4   5

Use the space below to reflect.

Spirit

(Filled
when
Saved)

Soul
mind will emotions

Spirit
will

Body

what comes out
when the
Spicket is
open

world

Romans 12

THE HOLY SPIRIT IN THE OLD TESTAMENT

· Genesis 1:2

The Hebrew word is *ruach* = breath, wind, presence of God

· *"Then the Lord said to Moses, 'See, I have chosen Bezalel son of Uri, the son of Hur, of the tribe of Judah, and I have filled him with the Spirit of God, with wisdom, with understanding, with knowledge and with all kinds of skills—to make artistic designs for work in gold, silver and bronze, to cut and set stones, to work in wood, and to engage in all kinds of crafts." (Exodus 31:2-5)*

· The Spirit repeatedly empowers the prophets in the Old Testament

· *"And afterward, I will pour out my Spirit on all people. Your sons and daughters will prophesy, your old men will dream dreams, your young men will see visions. Even on my servants, both men and women, I will pour out my Spirit in those days."* (Joel 2:28-29)

THE HOLY SPIRIT IN THE OLD TESTAMENT

· The Greek word is *pneuma* = similarly means breath, wind, presence of God

· *"[John the Baptist] will be filled with the HS even before he is born."* (Luke 1:15)

"The Holy Spirit will come on you, and the power of the Most High will over-shadow you." (Luke 1:35

· *"Just as Jesus was coming up out of the water, he saw heaven being torn open and the Spirit descending on him like a dove."* (Mark 1:10)

· *"The scroll of the prophet Isaiah was handed to him. Unrolling it, he found the place where it is written: 'The Spirit of the Lord is on me, because he has anointed me to proclaim good news to the poor. He has sent me to proclaim freedom for the prisoners and recovery of sight for the blind, to set the oppressed free, to proclaim the year of the Lord's favor.' Then he rolled up the scroll, gave it back to the attendant and sat down. The eyes of everyone in the synagogue were fastened on him. He began by saying to them, 'Today this scripture is fulfilled in your hearing.'"* (Luke 4:17-21)

· *"But if it is by the Spirit of God that I drive out demons, then the kingdom of God has come upon you."* (Matthew 12:28)

· *"Jesus said, 'Peace be with you! As the Father has sent me, I am sending you.' And with that he breathed on them and said, 'Receive the Holy Spirit...'"* (John 20:21-22)

· *"The Messiah will suffer and rise from the dead... repentance for the forgiveness of sins will be preached in his name to all nations.. .I am going to send you what my Father has promised; but stay in the city until you have been clothed with power from on high."* (Luke 24:46-49)

"Do not leave Jerusalem, but wait for the gift my Father promised, which you have heard me speak about. For John baptized with water, but in a few days you will be baptized with the Holy Spirit." (Acts 1:4-5)

When Jesus commissioned His disciples to go, He gave them authority, but they also needed to wait for empowering the Spirit.

· *"All of them were filled with the Holy Spirit and began to speak in other tongues as the Spirit enabled them."* (Acts 2:4)

DIFFERENCE BETWEEN HAVING HOLY SPIRIT AND BEING FILLED WITH HOLY SPIRIT

· We receive the Holy Spirit at salvation.

"When you believed, you were marked in him with a seal, the promised Holy Spirit, who is a deposit guaranteeing our inheritance." (Ephesians 1:13-14)

· Yet Acts speaks of people being saved who haven't yet heard of the Holy Spirit.

"Then Peter and John placed their hands on them, and they received the Holy Spirit." (Acts 8:14-17)

· When the Holy Spirit falls on people, supernatural gifts often break out.

"After the disciples prayed, the place where they were meeting was shaken. And they were filled with the HS and spoke the word of God boldly." (Acts 4:31)

"Do not get drunk on wine, which leads to debauchery. Instead, be filled with the Spirit, speaking to one another with psalms, hymns, and songs from the Spirit." (Ephesians 5:18)

"Be filled" is a...

» present =

» passive =

» imperative =

THE EFFECTS OF ALCOHOL VS THE EFFECTS OF THE HOLY SPIRIT

When we 'keep on being filled' with alcohol, it...
· Impacts our thinking
· Shapes our actions, and
· Causes us to do things we would not normally do.

Paul says don't let anything like alcohol do that to us! Only the Holy Spirit is meant to so direct us.

Instead, when we 'keep on being filled' with the Holy Spirit...
· God dominates our thoughts
· God shapes our actions, and
· God causes us to do things we would not - could not - normally do.

"So if you who are evil know how to give good gifts to your children, how much more will your Father in heaven give the Holy Spirit to those who ask Him!" (Luke 11:13)

Every Christian has the Holy Spirit, but not every Christian is filled with the Holy Spirit.

And God wants us to be filled up with the Holy Spirit!

PROCESSING TIME

Before we talk about how to be filled, what is your response to the teaching so far? What do you think about this instruction from Ephesians 5:18? Or the difference between having the Holy Spirit and being filled with the Holy Spirit?

Use the space below to reflect.

BLOCKING THE SPIRIT

· *"People who live by the Spirit"* (1 Corinthians 3:1)

· *"So I say, walk by the Spirit."* (Galatians 5:16)

· *"Keep in step with the Holy Spirit."* (Galatians 5:25)

· *"Do not quench the Spirit."* (1 Thessalonians 5:19)

WHAT DOES BLOCKING THE SPIRIT LOOK LIKE?

1. IGNORING HIM

2. PASSIVE BLOCKING

3. DISOBEDIENCE

4. UNHEALTHY CONTENTMENT

5. FEAR

HOW DO WE KEEP IN STEP WITH THE SPIRIT?

1. TIME

2. BIBLE

3. ASK AND SEEK

"If you then, though you are evil, know how to give good gifts to your children, how much more will your Father in heaven give the Holy Spirit to those who ask him!" (Luke 11:13)

4. OBEDIENCE

5. COMMUNITY

BEING FILLED: THERE'S ALWAYS ROOM FOR MORE!
We are like balloons!

John Stott: *"One baptism with many fillings"*

HOW TO BE FILLED WITH THE HOLY SPIRIT
Luke 11:9-13

EAGERLY DESIRE

ASK GOD

BELIEVE

PERSEVERE

WHEN DO WE PRAY FOR PEOPLE TO BE FILLED?

· Anytime!

· As someone comes to faith in Christ

· Immediately after someone is baptized

· At a time of commissioning

· After spiritual battle

· Unexpectedly!

HOMEWORK

Three overlapping things:

1. Take some time by yourself to ask God to fill you afresh with the Holy Spirit.

2. Ask someone else to pray for you to be filled afresh with the Holy Spirit.

3. Look for an opportunity to pray for someone else to be filled (afresh) with the Holy Spirit (e.g. in a weekend service, group, or individual conversation)

· Simply record what happened and what your experience was in each situation.

· Don't measure it by external manifestations, or even feelings.

· There are no expectations of you beyond asking God for more of His Spirit!

Record your experiences here.

Record your experiences here.

FURTHER DISCUSSION

We encourage you as a group to continue to process this content, along with other questions that you might have.

To help the conversation, here are a few stimulus questions:

1. What comes to mind when you think of the Holy Spirit?

2. Why is it important to "keep on being filled with the Holy Spirit"?

3. What can you do to keep more in step with the Spirit?

4. Have you ever prayed (or been prayed for) to be filled with the Spirit? If so, what happened?

5. Have you ever prayed for anyone to be filled with the Spirit? If so, what happened?

6. How would you respond to someone who asked to be filled with the Spirit?

MODULE B1:

Being Filled with the Holy Spirit

SESSION 2:

THE GIFT OF TONGUES

HOMEWORK REVIEW

Share your stories of what happened as you prayed for the infilling of the Holy Spirit.

Pray for each other and ask for more of the Spirit!

WHAT IS THE GIFT OF TONGUES?

· A form of prayer

"For anyone who speaks in a tongue does not speak to people but to God. Indeed, no one understands them; they utter mysteries by the Spirit."
(1 Corinthians 14:2)

· It's the connection of our spirit with God's Spirit

"The Spirit himself testifies with our spirit that we are God's children."
(Romans 8:16)

"For if I pray in a tongue, my spirit prays, but my mind is unfruitful."
(1 Corinthians 14:14

· The speaker is in full control

· It doesn't bypass your brain, it just bypasses the language you know.

TWO TYPES

"Though I speak with the tongues of men and angels..." (1 Corinthians 13:1)

1. HUMAN FOREIGN LANGUAGE

"Now there were staying in Jerusalem God-fearing Jews from every
nation under heaven. When they heard this sound, a crowd came
together in bewilderment, because each one heard their own language
being spoken." (Acts 2:5-6)

2. ANGELIC LANGUAGE

"We do not know what we ought to pray for, but the Spirit himself intercedes for us through wordless groans." (Romans 8:26)

SELF-ASSESSMENT

As you hear about speaking in tongues, on a scale of 1-5 (5=highly), how open do you feel to this gift and experience?

Circle your answer.

1   2   3   4   5

In 2s or 3s, or in the whole group, share why you picked that number.

Then discuss why you think tongues is perhaps the most controversial of the gifts of the Spirit.

CONNECTION TO BEING FILLED WITH THE SPIRIT

· Tongues is a Spirit-inspired utterance

· Classic Pentecostalism

· Sometimes in Acts people filled with the Holy Spirit begin to speak in tongues.

"All of them were filled with the Holy Spirit and began to speak in other tongues as the Spirit enabled them." (Acts 2:4)

· Paul seems to suggest that not everyone will speak in tongues.

"I would like every one of you to speak in tongues, but I would rather have you prophesy." (1 Corinthians 14:5)

· You can be filled with the Spirit, and able to hear the Lord in your life, even if you don't speak in tongues.

HOW THE GIFT OF TONGUES HELPS

1. PRAYER

"For if I pray in a tongue, my spirit prays, but my mind is unfruitful. So what shall I do? I will pray with my spirit, but I will also pray with my understanding." (1 Corinthians 14:14-15)

2. PRAISE

"The new believers in Cornelius' house began "speaking in tongues and praising God." (Acts 10:46)

3. WORSHIP

"I will sing with my spirit, but I will also sing with my understanding." (1 Corinthians 14:15)

4. WARFARE

"And pray in the Spirit on all occasions..." (Ephesians 6:18)

5. DELIVERANCE

e.g. Jackie Pullinger, *Chasing the Dragon*

6. INTERCESSION

7. SELF-EDIFICATION

"Anyone who speaks in a tongue edifies themselves." (1 Corinthians 14:4)

8. LANGUAGE LIMITS

""We do not know what we ought to pray for, but the Spirit himself intercedes for us through wordless groans." (Romans 8:26)

TONGUES IS USED IN TWO MAIN CONTEXTS

PRIVATE

"We do not know what we ought to pray for, but the Spirit himself intercedes for us through wordless groans." (Romans 8:26)

PUBLIC

"The one who prophesies is greater than the one who speaks in tongues, unless someone interprets, so that the church may be edified." (1 Corinthians 14:5)

"When you come together, each of you has a hymn, or a word of instruction, a revelation, a tongue or an interpretation. Everything must be done so that the church may be built up." (1 Corinthians 14:26-28)

THE GOAL OF THE GIFT IS EDIFICATION

"I would like everyone of you to speak in tongues, (but I would rather have you prophesy." (1 Corinthians 14:5)

"Anyone who speaks in a tongue edifies themselves, (but the one who prophesies edifies the church)." (1 Corinthians 14:4)

"BUT I WAS TAUGHT, 'TONGUES ARE OF THE DEVIL'"

Judge it like any other aspect of our faith: by the fruit.

WHEN THE GIFT OF TONGUES IS ABUSED

Much damage has been done by people using the gift of tongues as a way to judge others.

I must be careful not to impose my experience of the gifts upon others.

> (e.g. questioning someone's salvation because they
> don't speak in tongues)

PROCESSING TIME

As you've listened to us teach so far, what has most impacted you? What have you found helpful - and what aren't you sure about?

Use the space below to reflect.

In your room, whether in 2s or 3s, or as a whole group, take a few minutes to share some of your responses.

Use the space below to take notes and reflect.

TIPS ON HOW TO RECEIVE THIS GIFT

· SUPERNATURAL DOWNLOAD

· ENGAGEMENT FROM OUR END

1. Pray

2. Cooperate

+ Learn from others who already have the gift.

3. Worship

4. Practice

OTHER POINTS TO CONSIDER

· Everything new is weird at first!

· 'Play' with it

· It's a tool in our toolbox

· Don't feel pressured to do it perfectly

· Our heart posture is the thing that matters

THE GIFT OF INTERPRETATION OF TONGUES

Interpretation of tongues is a gift of the Spirit.

Think of it as under the broader umbrella of prophecy, since it is about receiving supernatural revelation from God and sharing it appropriately.

The interpreter might be:

- The person who has the tongue, or it might be someone else

- Usually it comes across like a prophetic word being shared

- Notably, any interpretation in a public gathering should be strengthening, encouraging, and comforting

WHAT TO DO IF A TONGUE IS SHARED IN A PUBLIC GATHERING

- Keep calm and peaceful!

- Explain what just happened

- Say we're going to wait together for a moment to see if someone has an interpretation

- Either: there's an interpretation, or no more tongues that day

HOMEWORK

Here are some links to tongues being used in worship. If these aren't helpful, just ignore them!

But you might want to find that place where you are not being overheard, and play one or some of them, and seek to join in with the worship leader, both when in English and when in tongues. Don't worry about saying the "right" words, as no-one else is listening.

To be honest, the goal is not for you to speak tongues! Instead, the goal is for you to encounter the Lord in worship and to honor Him. Thus success in this exercise is drawing closer to Jesus and loving Him more deeply, whether or not you find speak in tongues.

Grace upon grace to you!

Cory Asbury - Always Faithful (Prophetic Song)
(around 1 minute 25 seconds in)

https://www.youtube.com/watch?v=Dm5Jatw_xNQ

John Mark Pantana - Let My Love
(just over 1 minute in)

https://www.youtube.com/watch?v=P5NXAypMOq8

Jenn Johnson - Joy Of The Lord
(from near the start)

https://www.youtube.com/watch?v=982z7KRkb7g

Melissa Helser - Catch The Wind
(about 3 minutes 20 seconds in)

https://www.youtube.com/watch?v=FBeZwQgWtcA

FURTHER DISCUSSION

We encourage you as a group to continue to process this content, along with other questions that you might have.

To help the conversation, here are a few stimulus questions:

1. What do you think of when speaking in tongues is mentioned?

2. Do you have any experiences with the gift of tongues? If so, how did it make you feel?

3. How would you answer someone who thinks that tongues is a demonic deception?

4. How would you coach someone who spoke loudly in tongues in every worship or prayer gathering?

5. What would you do if someone spoke in tongues to a group you were leading?

6. How would you assess whether someone has interpreted a tongue correctly?

MODULE B2:

Spiritual Warfare

SESSION 1:

BIBLICAL WAYS TO
UNDERSTAND BATTLE

HOMEWORK REVIEW

What insights or questions about tongues come up as a result of spending time in worship?

"All authority in heaven and on earth has been given to me. Therefore go and make disciples of all nations." (Matthew 28:18-29)

Making disciples is spiritual warfare!

Our God is at war - and you've been drafted into His army!

Yet, through it all, Jesus assures us of His presence and eternal protection. *"And surely I am with you always, to the very end of the age"* (Matthew 28:20)

WHO IS OUR GOD?

Spiritual warfare begins with a right understanding of the nature of God.

He is the uncreated one, the creator of everything and every being.

He is all-knowing, all-powerful, and everywhere-present.

"The Lord is good to all; he has compassion on all he has made." (Psalm 145:9)

He is a God who will do anything, including going to war, both to bring us back into the family of God and also to bring about the fullness of His good rule in this world and the next.

We are not just offered salvation from our sins, but an entry into an eternity of purposeful and productive living, in a breath-taking partnership with Him.

"I have come that they may have life, and have it to the full." (John 10:10)

We are empowered to fight God's battles.

"With God we will gain the victory, and he will trample down our enemies." (Psalm 60:12)

"But the Lord is faithful, and he will strengthen you and protect you from the evil one." (2 Thessalonians 3:3)

SELF-ASSESSMENT

On a scale of 1 to 10, where 1 = "I never really think about it", and 10 = "Isn't almost everything in life part of a cosmic spiritual battle?", overall how do you experience spiritual warfare in your life?

Circle your answer.

1	2	3	4	5
6	7	8	9	10

Use the space below to reflect.

BIBLICAL TEACHING ABOUT SATAN

Satan means adversary, or one who resists.

He is also called the devil, which means slanderer, since one of his favorite tactics is to sow lies and distort the truth.

"He was a murderer from the beginning, not holding to the truth, for there is no truth in him. When he lies, he speaks his native language, for he is a liar and the father of lies." (John 8:44)

BIBLE REFERENCES ABOUT SATAN AND HIS NAMES

· Serpent — *"Now the serpent was more crafty than any of the wild animals the Lord God had made."* (Genesis 3:1)

· Adversary — he is opposed to humanity (Job 1)

· Lucifer —meaning *'bearer of light'* or *'day star'* (Isaiah 14:12)

· He was originally very beautiful — *"You were the seal of perfection, full of wisdom and perfect in beauty."* (Ezekiel 28:12).

· Tempter — *"The tempter came to him and said, 'If you are the Son of God, tell these stones to become bread.'"* (Matthew 4:3)

· Devil — 'accuser,' *"If you are the Son of God..."* (Matthew 4:6)

· Beelzebul - literally, *'lord of dung'* or *'lord of flies'*! (Mark 3:22)

· Ruler (or prince) of the demons (Mark 3:22)

· Evil one (Matthew 13:19)

· God of this age — *"The god of this age has blinded the minds of unbelievers."* (2 Corinthians 4:4)

· Belial — means *'worthless'* or *'wicked'* (2 Corinthians 6:15)

· Ruler of the kingdom of the air — *"When you followed the ways of this world and of the ruler of the kingdom of the air, the spirit who is now at work in those who are disobedient."* (Ephesians 2:2)

· Roaring lion looking for someone to devour (1 Peter 5:8)

· Dragon — *"Then I saw an angel coming down from heaven, having the key to the bottomless pit and a great chain in his hand. He laid hold of the dragon, that serpent of old, who is the Devil and Satan, and bound him for a thousand years."* (Revelation 20:1-2)

This gives us a clear view of his nature and values!

WHAT THIS MEANS

1. THE DEVIL IS A SPIRITUAL BEING WHO IS THE SOURCE OF ALL EVIL

2. ORIGINALLY HE WAS AN ANGEL CREATED BY GOD

3. LUCIFER WANTED TO BE LIKE GOD.
   Isaiah 14:3-2, Ezekiel 28:12-19

4. SATAN AND HIS DEMONS SEEK TO ATTACK AND TEAR DOWN HUMANS, AS WELL AS THE GOODNESS OF THIS CREATED WORLD

"Your enemy the devil prowls around like a roaring lion looking for someone to devour." (1 Peter 5:8)

"The whole world is under the control of the evil one." (1 John 5:19)

3 THINGS SATAN IS NOT

OMNIPRESENT (ALWAYS PRESENT)

"And the Lord said to Satan, 'From where do you come?' So, Satan answered the Lord and said, 'From going to and fro on the earth, and from walking back and forth on it.'" (Job 1:7)

"When the devil had finished all this tempting, he left him until an opportune time." (Luke 4:13)

If Satan Is Not Omnipresent, Why Is the Presence of Evil Everywhere?

1. He has an army of helpers (demons)

2. Sin has infected the structures of creation and culture, so we see that worked out all around us (Romans 1)

3. We sin and sometimes the consequences of our choices open the doorway to the enemy to oppress us

4. Ephesians 6:12 talks about a range of enemy forces — rulers, authorities, powers, and spiritual forces — which implies they operate at different levels of culture and society.

OMNIPOTENT (ALL POWERFUL)

"And having disarmed the powers and authorities, he made a public spectacle of them, triumphing over them by the cross." (Colossians 2:15)

He will receive his final and eternal punishment. *"And the devil, who deceived them, was thrown into the lake of burning sulfur, where the beast and the false prophet had been thrown. They will be tormented day and night for ever and ever."* (Revelation 20:10)

OMNISCIENT (ALL KNOWING)

"For who knows a person's thoughts except their own spirit within them? In the same way no one knows the thoughts of God except the Spirit of God." (1 Corinthians 2:11)

The enemy doesn't know our thoughts, but he does know our weaknesses. He tries to put certain thoughts in my mind.

THE CENTRALITY OF THE CROSS

The cross of Jesus is the pivotal point of all spiritual warfare.

- The first prophecy given announced what Jesus would do: that a descendant of Eve would utterly defeat the devil *"he will crush your head"* (Genesis 3:15).

- The central thing Jesus did was drive out the *"prince of this world"* (John 12:31).

- Jesus was determined to *"destroy the works of the devil"* (1 John 3:8), and to *"destroy the one who has the power of death, that is, the devil"* (Hebrews 2:14)

- Jesus did this in order to *"free those who all their lives were held in slavery by the fear of death"* (Hebrews 2:14-15).

- Jesus established a new reign that would ultimately *"put all his enemies under his feet"* (1 Corinthians 15:25).

- Though *"the strong man"* was *"fully armed,"* one who was "stronger than he" had finally arrived who could *"attack and overpower him"* (Luke 11:21-22).

- While the *"thief comes only to steal and kill and destroy,"* Jesus came into the world to vanquish the thief so that all *"may have life and have it abundantly"* (John 10:10).

- Jesus *"disarmed the rulers and authorities and made a public example of them, triumphing over them…"* (Colossians 2:15).

Until Jesus returns, we continue to battle *"against the rulers, against the authorities, against the powers of this dark world and against the spiritual forces of evil in the heavenly realms."* (Ephesians 6:12)

This is why we find ourselves participants in spiritual warfare.

DEFINING SPIRITUAL WARFARE

DEFINITION

Spiritual warfare is the recognition that we are part of a cosmic battle between Jesus' actively advancing kingly rule, and the retreating but still viciously wicked opposition of the evil one. Until we reach the 2nd Coming of Jesus, we find ourselves in this in-between time, where we join God's forces in driving back the ultimately defeated demonic forces of Satan.

"When evening comes, you say, 'It will be fair weather, for the sky is red,' and in the morning, 'Today it will be stormy, for the sky is red and overcast.' You know how to interpret the appearance of the sky, but you cannot interpret the signs of the times." (Matthew 16:2-3)

We must become more adept in understanding the spiritual realm than we do the purely natural realm.

YOUR EXPERIENCE

What does spiritual warfare mean to you? What stories do you have of
spiritual warfare?

Use the space below to take notes and reflect.

In 2s or 3s, or in the whole group, share some of your stories or experiences.
As you do so, make sure that the star of the story and hero is Jesus, rather than
you or, far worse, the devil.

IT'S NOT JUST DEFENSE!

"And from the time John the Baptist began preaching until now, the Kingdom of Heaven has been forcefully advancing, and violent people are attacking it." (Matthew 11:12)

Jesus invites us to be amongst the aggressive ones who are actively taking hold of that coming Kingdom, seeking more of its presence to be revealed in and through our lives.

Many Christians take on a siege mentality, whereby they circle the wagons and hunker down, waiting for the cavalry to arrive with the second coming of Christ.

"And I tell you, you are Peter, and on this rock I will build my church, and the gates of hell shall not prevail against it." (Matthew 16:18)

OFFENSIVE WARFARE

· Prayer and worship

· Sharing the Gospel

· Healing the sick

· Bringing hope where people have given up

· Deliverance

· Anything that takes ground from the enemy

"He has sent me to proclaim freedom for the prisoners and recovery of sight for the blind, to set the oppressed free." (Luke 4:18)

"Heal the sick, raise the dead, cleanse those who have leprosy, drive out demons." (Matthew 10:8)

OLD TESTAMENT VS NEW TESTAMENT WARFARE

Often warfare in the Old Testament is physical battle, whereas in the New Testament the same lessons apply spiritually.

JOSHUA 1: The Israelites going into the promised land, facing battle of Jericho

· Be strong and courageous

· Consecrate yourselves

· The Lord leads the way - sometimes He may use strange tactics!

· The authority we carry flows from our prompt obedience

DEFENSIVE WARFARE

When you're under attack. Sometimes the smart strategy is to take cover.

However, none of this is an excuse to permanently operate in defensive mode.

CONSIDER: Are we operating as a force or a fortress?

We're called to be a force, with Jesus as our fortress!

PICTURE OF A BATTLE SCENE

· Who are you fighting and what are your orders?

· Listen for the fresh word of God for this situation

· Don't be intimidated by the enemy

· During the battle, keep your focus - what is your Captain saying?

· Respond immediately to his call

· Have an underlying, unwavering faith and trust in Him and His overall plan

QUESTION: WHAT IS SPIRITUAL WARFARE AND WHAT IS MURPHY'S LAW?

Murphy's Law states that "anything that can go wrong will go wrong". This is where discernment is key.

Some see a demon behind every cushion, which is an excessive response.

"In this world you will have trouble. But take heart! I have overcome the world." (John 16:33b)

To discern the cause, you should:

1. Pray and ask God what's going on

2. Look for patterns of negative things that feel sinister

3. Talk to others - See if someone with the gift of discernment senses something

4. The thoughts Satan brings are marked by destruction

5. Ask: is this incident simply a result of living in a fallen world?

Spiritual warfare is real. We have an enemy — but we have a far greater and more powerful God. We should not be ignorant or fearful of this realm, because we need to know how to fight and take ground for King Jesus.

HOMEWORK

For the next two weeks, ask the Lord to show you spiritual warfare going on around you (offensive and defensive). This doesn't necessarily mean you have to join in - the aim is to be 'seeing' more into the unseen spiritual realm.

Ask God to show you the strategies for fighting the enemy that either others are using, or which you have used/do use. Bring these to our next conversation, where we'll move into the practicalities of fighting the battle.

Record thoughts and experiences here.

BONUS — If you're more creatively wired, listen to and meditate on this song by Jess Ray. Why is it shot in Jerusalem? To which Biblical story is 'gallows' referring?

Search online for, "Jess Ray, Gallows (live in Jerusalem)" or use this link: https://www.youtube.com/watch?v=5pupsopSaJ8

FURTHER DISCUSSION

We encourage you as a group to continue to process this content, along with other questions that you might have.

To help the conversation, here are a few stimulus questions:

1. Do you think of God as being at war? Why?

2. Is the idea of an actual physical devil one that you agree with? How would you describe who he is to a new believer?

3. Have you considered the 'victory over satan' side of the cross before? What do you find powerful about that angle on the cross?

4. Do you tend to see spiritual warfare as primarily defensive or offensive?

5. How do you most effectively operate in offensive warfare?

6. What do you think is the difference between Murphy's Law and spiritual warfare?

MODULE B2:

Spiritual Warfare

SESSION 2:

HOW TO DEVELOP
WISE WARFARE STRATEGIES

HOMEWORK REVIEW

What spiritual warfare (offensive and defensive) did the Lord reveal to you?

What strategies for fighting the enemy did you think of?

WARFARE IS REAL

Jesus *"went around doing good and healing all who were under the power of the devil."* (Acts 10:38)

There is a spiritual realm, there is a personal force of evil that brings oppression into all lives, but our God is far stronger and greater!

However, today we live in the in-between times, when Jesus has won the victory over all evil at the cross, but this won't be fully made manifest until His second coming.

> » January 1, 1863 — The Emancipation Proclamation
>
> » December 6, 1865 - The 13th Amendment is ratified
>
> *In between — three terrible years of fighting and loss.*

You have been drafted into God's army and called to fight with boldness, wisdom, and persistence to enforce the victory of Jesus.

SOME BIBLICAL EXAMPLES OF SPIRITUAL WARFARE

· Adam & Eve (Genesis 3)

· Moses and pharoah's priests (Exodus 7-12)

· Israel fighting the Amalekites (Exodus 17:8-16)

· Walls of Jericho (Joshua 6)

· Elisha's servant can't see the angels surrounding them (2 Kings 6)

· Elijah and the prophets of Baal, and then extreme depression and discouragement (1 Kings 18,19)

· Sanballat opposing Nehemiah and the rebuilding of the walls (Nehemiah 4)

· Job

· *"Then he continued, 'Do not be afraid, Daniel. Since the first day that you set your mind to gain understanding and to humble yourself before your God, your words were heard, and I have come in response to them. But the prince of the Persian kingdom resisted me twenty-one days. Then Michael, one of the chief princes, came to help me, because I was detained there with the king of Persia. Now I have come to explain to you what will happen to your people in the future, for the vision concerns a time yet to come...So he said, 'Do you know why I have come to you? Soon I will return to fight against the prince of Persia, and when I go, the prince of Greece will come; but first I will tell you what is written in the Book of Truth. No one supports me against them except Michael, your prince.'"* (Daniel 10:12-14, 20-21)

· "But even the archangel Michael, when he was disputing with the devil about the body of Moses, did not himself dare to condemn him for slander but said, 'The Lord rebuke you!'" (Jude 1:9)

· Temptation of Jesus (Luke 4)

· In Philippi a demon possessed slave girl *"followed Paul and the rest of us, shouting, 'These men are servants of the Most High God, who are telling you the way to be saved.' She kept this up for many days. Finally Paul became so annoyed that he turned around and said to the spirit, 'In the name of Jesus Christ I command you to come out of her!' At that moment the spirit left her."* (Acts 16:17-18)

· *"For we wanted to come to you - certainly I, Paul, did, again and again - but Satan blocked our way."* (1 Thessalonians 2:18)

- *"For our struggle is not against flesh and blood, but against the rulers, against the authorities, against the powers of this dark world and against the spiritual forces of evil in the heavenly realms."* (Ephesians 6:12)

- *"I saw heaven standing open and there before me was a white horse, whose rider is called Faithful and True. With justice he judges and wages war... The armies of heaven were following him, riding on white horses and dressed in fine linen, white and clean."* (Revelation 19:11,14).

DON'T...

1. Fear or get stressed

2. Give up or withdraw

3. Lose hope

4. Get distracted (stay steadfast)

5. Focus on the enemy

CONTEXT IS EVERYTHING

Our physical and cultural context will affect how spiritual warfare looks and feels. This is because not every place or organization has the same vulnerabilities, and so they face different types of spiritual battles.

YOUR EXPERIENCE

Why do you think spiritual warfare looks so different in different contexts?

What are some of the patterns that you've seen and experienced?

In 2s or 3s, or in the whole group, share some of your stories or experiences. As you do so, make sure that the star of the story and hero is Jesus, rather than you or, far worse, the devil.

Use the space below to take notes and reflect.

WHAT ARE THE ENEMY'S STRATEGIES?

Essentially the enemy tries to destroy / hinder / slow down...

- The goodness of God's creation plan

- People committing to Christ as Savior and Lord

- People maturing and growing in their walk with Jesus

- The advance of God's Kingdom and the renewal of all things

The devil's GOAL: even if we remain saved and don't just give up, he hopes we will at least not try as hard as we can.

TWO MAIN BATTLEGROUNDS

"The weapons we fight with are not the weapons of the world. On the contrary, they have divine power to demolish strongholds. We demolish arguments and every pretension that sets itself up against the knowledge of God, and we take captive every thought to make it obedient to Christ." (2 Corinthians 10:4-5)

THE BATTLE OF THE MIND

» *"Did God really say...?"* (Genesis 3:1)

» *"If you are the Son of God..."* (Matthew 4:6)

"The weapons we fight with are not the weapons of the world. On the contrary, they have divine power to demolish strongholds. We demolish arguments and every pretension that sets itself up against the knowledge of God, and we take captive every thought to make it obedient to Christ." 2 Corinthians 10:4-5

Q. HOW DOES SATAN GIVE ME THOUGHTS?

· Temptation

· My weaknesses

· Bombardments that batter us down

· Circumstances of life

"A spiritual stronghold is a mindset impregnated with hopelessness which causes us to accept as unchangeable, situations that we know are contrary to the will of God." (Ed Silvoso)

THE BATTLEGROUND OF RELATIONSHIPS

Paul writes that *"in order to keep me from becoming conceited, I was given a thorn in my flesh, a messenger of Satan, to torment me."* (2 Corinthians 12:7)

"My grace is sufficient for you, for my power is made perfect in weakness." (2 Corinthians 12:8).

"That is why, for Christ's sake, I delight in weaknesses, in insults, in hardships, in persecutions, in difficulties. For when I am weak, then I am strong." (2 Corinthians 12:10)

» Paul describes the weaknesses (thorns in the flesh) that God allows in purely relational terms.

» The "thorn in the flesh" (or side) appears in Joshua 23:13 and Ezekiel 28:24. On both occasions it is in reference to neighboring tribes who were opposed to the work of God

"I have been constantly on the move. I have been in danger from rivers, in danger from bandits, in danger from my fellow Jews, in danger from Gentiles; in danger in the city, in danger in the country, in danger at sea; and in danger from false believers. I have labored and toiled and have often gone without sleep; I have known hunger and thirst and have often gone without food; I have been cold and naked." (2 Corinthians 11:26-27).

HERE'S HOW TO OVERCOME

1. Recognize when there's a particular way of thinking that is not growing you closer to Jesus and Christlikeness

2. Ask Jesus for His perspective on that situation and person

3. I must take that thought captive by replacing it with God's perspective

4. I must massage and work this greater truth deep into my innermost being

5. It is so easy to flip from a Kingdom mindset whereby we forget that we are children of God, beloved, and with an amazing future

YOUR EXPERIENCE

Where do you tend to most experience spiritual battle - relationships, the mind, or somewhere else?

In 2s or 3s, or in the whole group, share some of your stories or experiences. As you do so, make sure that the star of the story and hero is Jesus, rather than you or, far worse, the devil.

Use the space below to take notes and reflect.

GENERAL PREPARATION

THE EAGLE VS THE POISONOUS SNAKE

Take your fight into the spiritual realm by praying.

IN ADVANCE

"And lead us not into temptation, but deliver us from the evil one." (Matthew 6:13)

"Finally, be strong in the Lord and in his mighty power. Put on the full armor of God, so that you can take your stand against the devil's schemes. For our struggle is not against flesh and blood, but against the rulers, against the authorities, against the powers of this dark world and against the spiritual forces of evil in the heavenly realms.

Therefore put on the full armor of God, so that when the day of evil comes, you may be able to stand your ground, and after you have done everything, to stand.

Stand firm then, with the belt of truth buckled around your waist, with the breastplate of righteousness in place, and with your feet fitted with the readiness that comes from the gospel of peace. In addition to all this, take up the shield of faith, with which you can extinguish all the flaming arrows of the evil one. Take the helmet of salvation and the sword of the Spirit, which is the word of God. And pray in the Spirit on all occasions with all kinds of prayers and requests. With this in mind, be alert and always keep on praying for all the Lord's people." (Ephesians 6:10-18)

· Belt of truth — know the truth of who God is, who you are, and He wants you to live

· Breastplate of righteousness — right relationship with Jesus

· Feet fitted with the readiness — we are to be proactive in advancing God's Kingdom

· Shield of faith — have unwavering faith that God is at work

· Helmet of salvation —allow Jesus to save every part of our humanity

· Sword of the Spirit — God's eternal word through Scripture, and also His specific personal 'now' word

· Pray in the Spirit — ask the Spirit to guide you in your prayers

· Be alert - what's Jesus saying and doing? What's He up to?

· Pray for each other - in an alert, attentive way

» Using the framework of the spiritual armor, we can daily proactively prepare and train for spiritual battle.

STRATEGIES FOR WHEN YOU'RE IN THE BATTLE

1. SCRIPTURE

2. SPIRITUAL ARMOR

3. PRAYER (INCLUDING PRAYER WALKING)

"So Peter was kept in prison, but the church was earnestly praying to God for him." (Acts 12:5)

4. FASTING

"This kind can only come out by prayer and fasting" (Matthew 17:21)

5. TONGUES

"And pray in the Spirit on all occasions with all kinds of prayers and requests." (Ephesians 6:18)

6. "TAKE EVERY THOUGHT CAPTIVE"

(2 Corinthians 10:5)

7. COMMAND ANY SPIRITS TO LEAVE IN THE NAME OF JESUS

"Away from me, Satan!" (Matthew 4:10)

8. REPLACE LIES WITH TRUTH

"And you will know the truth, and the truth will set you free." (John 8:32)

9. REPENT AND FORGIVE

"Anyone you forgive, I also forgive. And what I have forgiven I have forgiven in the sight of Christ for your sake, in order that Satan might not outwit us. For we are not unaware of his schemes." (2 Corinthians 2:10,11)

10. FOCUS

"Finally, brothers and sisters, whatever is true, whatever is noble, whatever is right, whatever is pure, whatever is lovely, whatever is admirable—if anything is excellent or praiseworthy—think about such things." (Philippians 4:8)

11. FOCUS ON CHRIST'S SUFFERING OVER MINE

"Consider him who endured such opposition from sinners, so that you will not grow weary and lose heart." (Hebrews 12:3)

12. OPERATE FROM LOVE

"Do not be overcome with evil, but overcome evil with good." (Romans 12:14)

"Bless those who persecute you; bless and do not curse." (Romans 12:21)

13. MOVE IN THE OPPOSITE SPIRIT OF WHAT'S GOING ON

14. CHOOSE JOY

"Consider it pure joy, my brothers and sisters, whenever you face trials of many kinds" (James 1:2)

15. COMMUNITY

"Bear one another's burdens" (Galatians 6:2)

16. TESTIMONY

"They triumphed over him by the blood of the Lamb and by the word of their testimony." (Revelation 12:11)

17. PROPHETIC WORDS

"Timothy, my son, I am giving you this command in keeping with the prophecies once made about you, so that by recalling them you may fight the battle well." (1 Timothy 1:18)

18. CHOOSE BOLDNESS NOT FEAR

The believers' prayer after Peter and John are released from prison (Acts 4:23-31)

19. TAKE THE FIGHT TO THE ENEMY

"I will build my church, and the gates of Hades will not overcome it." (Matthew 16:18

20. COMMUNION

21. ANOINTING OIL

22. HOLY WATER

23. INCENSE

24. DEAL WITH IT

"My grace is sufficient for you, for my power is made perfect in weakness." (2 Corinthians 12:9)

25. SURRENDER YOURSELF TO GOD

"Submit yourselves to God. Resist the devil, and he will flee from you." (James 4:7)

Jesus at Gethsemane: *"'Abba, Father,' he said, 'everything is possible for you. Take this cup from me. Yet not what I will, but what you will'."* (Mark 14:36)

26. WORSHIP AND PRAISE

"About midnight Paul and Silas were praying and singing hymns to God." (Acts 16:25)

27. THANKSGIVING

"Do not be anxious about anything, but in every situation, by prayer and petition, with thanksgiving, present your requests to God." (Philippians 4:6)

28. WAIT ON THE LORD

"But they who wait for the Lord shall renew their strength." (Isaiah 40:31)

29. KEEP SOLDIERING ON!

WHEN SHOULD YOU EMPLOY WHICH TACTICS?

· Pray and ask God for wisdom

· Ask other people around you

· Try different strategies

· Surrender and worship

HOMEWORK

"The weapons we fight with are not the weapons of the world. On the contrary, they have divine power to demolish strongholds. We demolish arguments and every pretension that sets itself up against the knowledge of God, and we take captive every thought to make it obedient to Christ." (2 Corinthians 10:4-5)

Ask the Lord for your next step in growing in spiritual warfare (whether offensive or defensive), specifically if there is an area for you to push into.

Look at the above list of strategies for fighting with the Lord's weapons (NB this is not an exhaustive list.

FURTHER DISCUSSION

We encourage you as a group to continue to process this content, along with other questions that you might have.

To help the conversation, here are a few stimulus questions:

1. Tell some stories of when you have engaged in offensive warfare to actively advance the Kingdom.

2. What are some of the strategies that the enemy uses in your life to pull you away from Jesus?

3. How does the battle of the mind manifest itself in your life?

4. How does the battle of relationships express itself in your life?

5. What do you specifically need to do to prepare in advance of the battle?

6. What strategies have you successfully used in the past to overcome the schemes of the enemy?

MODULE B3:

How to Discern and Drive Out Demons

SESSION 1:

BIBLICAL AND PRACTICAL FOUNDATIONS

HOMEWORK REVIEW

What insights or questions come up as a result of processing how to grow in spiritual warfare?

———————

All over the world, and throughout history, in most cultures there has been a recognition of a spirit realm.

In the Lord's Prayer, it is "Deliver us from the evil one" (there's a definite article there), yet most English translations call it evil in the abstract.

BASIC EQUIPPING

This is a basic thing. We're not trying to get you to an advanced level. But we do want you to be able to be obedient to Jesus as He repeatedly tells us to drive out demons.

DELIVERANCE IN THE BIBLE

There are 20ish accounts of deliverance in the gospels, 5 more in Acts, plus many more throughout church history.

JESUS AND DELIVERANCE

- *"The Spirit of the Lord is on me, because he has anointed me to proclaim good news to the poor. He has sent me to proclaim freedom for the prisoners and recovery of sight for the blind, to set the oppressed free, to proclaim the year of the Lord's favor."* (Luke 4:18-19)

- Jesus starts his public ministry in the synagogue in Capernaum by casting an impure spirit out of a man (Luke 4:31-37)

- *"News about (Jesus) spread all over Syria, and people brought to him all who were ill with various diseases, those suffering severe pain, the demon-possessed, those having seizures, and the paralyzed; and he healed them."* (Matthew 4:24)

- *"When evening came, many who were demon-possessed were brought to him, and he drove out the spirits with a word and healed all the sick."* (Matthew 8:16)

- *"While they were going out, a man who was demon-possessed and could not talk was brought to Jesus. And when the demon was driven out, the man who had been mute spoke."* (Matthew 9:22-23)

· *"Then they brought him a demon-possessed man who was blind and mute, and Jesus healed him, so that he could both talk and see."* (Matthew 12:22)

· Jesus sets the Canaanite woman's daughter free (Matthew 15:21-28)

· After healing Peter's mother-in-law *"The whole town gathered at the door, and Jesus healed many who had various diseases. He also drove out many demons, but he would not let the demons speak because they knew who he was.... So he traveled throughout Galilee, preaching in their synagogues and driving out demons."* (Mark 1:32-34, 39)

· The man called Legion (Mark 5:1-20)

· *"The Twelve were with him, and also some women who had been cured of evil spirits and diseases"* (Luke 8:2)

· Jesus heals the crippled woman on the sabbath in the Synagogue (Luke 13:10-13)

EXAMPLES FROM THE APOSTLES AND THE EARLY CHURCH:

· *"Crowds gathered also from the towns around Jerusalem, bringing their sick and those tormented by impure spirits, and all of them were healed."* (Acts 5:16)

· *"Philip went down to a city in Samaria and proclaimed the Messiah there... with shrieks, impure spirits came out of many, and many who were paralyzed or lame were healed."* (Acts 8:5, 7)

· A demonized slave girl keeps on shouting at the apostles. *"Finally Paul became so annoyed that he turned around and said to the spirit, 'In the name of Jesus Christ I command you to come out of her!' At that moment the spirit left her."* (Acts 16:16-18)

· *"God did extraordinary miracles through Paul, so that even handkerchiefs and aprons that had touched him were taken to the sick, and their illnesses were cured and the evil spirits left them."* (Acts 19:11-12)

· Several Jews, including the 7 sons of Sceva *"who went around driving out evil spirits tried to invoke the name of the Lord Jesus over those who were demon-possessed...One day the evil spirit answered them, 'Jesus I know, and Paul I know about, but who are you?'"* It then jumped on and overpowered them! (Acts 19:13-16)

· *"Put on the full armor of God, so that you can take your stand against the devil's schemes. For our struggle is not against flesh and blood, but against the rulers, against the authorities, against the powers of this dark world and against the spiritual forces of evil in the heavenly realms."* (Ephesians 6:11-12)

· *"And having disarmed the powers and authorities, he made a public spectacle of them, triumphing over them by the cross."* (Colossians 2:15)

PROCESSING TIME

Is deliverance a part of your walk with the Lord?

On a scale of 1-5, where 1 is that you never pray for deliverance and 5 is that you regularly do, how would you score yourself?

Circle your answer.

1   2   3   4   5

In your room, whether in 2s or 3s, or as a whole group, take a few minutes to share some of your responses.

WHAT ARE DEMONS?

A demon is a supernatural creature who rebelled against the sovereignty of God, and who aligned itself with Lucifer.

"They do not differ in nature from good angels, but their nature is depraved." (CS Lewis)

DELIVERANCE MINISTRY OVERVIEW

Deliverance is part of what Jesus sent us out to do.

In fact, whenever Jesus talks about going with the gospel He almost always ties it to healing and driving out demons.

· The disciples' purpose: *"He appointed twelve that they might be with him and that he might send them out to preach and to have authority to drive out demons."* (Mark 3:14-15)

· *"Calling the Twelve to him, he began to send them out two by two and gave them authority over impure spirits... They went out and preached that people should repent. They drove out many demons and anointed many sick people with oil and healed them."* (Mark 6:7, 12-13)

· "He said to them, 'Go into all the world and preach the gospel to all creation... And these signs will accompany those who believe: In my name they will drive out demons; they will speak in new tongues; they will pick up snakes with their hands; and when they drink deadly poison, it will not hurt them at all; they will place their hands on sick people, and they will get well.'" (Mark 16:15-18)

The story of Scripture is that of God's acting to bring deliverance to His people.

Jesus is our Savior, our bondage breaker, our deliverer, and our liberator.

· **Deliverance is needed** — (Luke 4:19-10, John 14:12, 20:21).

· **Calling**

· **Ignorance** — "I do not want you to be uninformed" about spiritual things (1 Corinthians 12:1)

· **Fear, Flight or Fight**

· **Identity** — "One day the evil spirit answered them, 'Jesus I know, and Paul I know about, but who are you?'" (Acts 19:13-16)

· **Obedience**

· **Be Spirit-Led**

5 LEVELS OF DEMONIC INFLUENCE

In the ministry of Jesus, He is clear that some sickness - whether mental, emotional or physical - is caused by demonic activity. Such enemy activity comes at a variety of levels:

1. TEMPTATION

"[Jesus] has been tempted in every way, just as we are - yet he did not sin." (Hebrews 4:15)

2. HARASSMENT

Like flies (Beelzebub)

3. OPPRESSION

Attack like a band around your head

4. HABITATION (YOU'RE DEMONIZED)

It's there & has influence

5. POSSESSION

Not Christians (because it's about ownership) —dominating control

PROCESSING TIME

As you've listened to us teach so far, what has most impacted you?

What have you found helpful - and what aren't you sure about?

In your room, whether in 2s or 3s, or as a whole group, take a few minutes to share some of your responses. It's okay if not everyone is at the same place - this is how we learn from one another.

HOW DO YOU KNOW?

These things can be signs (but it doesn't always mean the demonic is present):

1. BLOCKED PRAYERS

2. DISCERNMENT

3. EXTREME RESPONSES - IRRATIONAL EMOTIONS OR EXTREME ATTITUDES

4. NIGHTMARES

5. COMPULSIONS AND ADDICTIONS

6. CHRONIC PHYSICAL SICKNESS

7. PATTERNS

8. OCCULT/ OTHER RELIGIONS

9. FAMILY HISTORY

10. RESPONSE TO SACRED THINGS

11. DISUNITY

12. STRANGER THINGS

13. PERSONALITY CHANGES

14. CONTORTED PHYSICAL REACTIONS

THE GIFT OF DISCERNMENT/DISCERNING BETWEEN SPIRITS

"...to another distinguishing between spirits..." (1 Corinthians 12:10)

HOW TO GROW IN THIS GIFT:

· ASK FOR IT

· BRING A LISTENING POSTURE

· PRACTICE.

"But solid food is for the mature, who because of practice have their senses trained to distinguish between good and evil." (Matthew 5:14, NASB)

· "LORD, THIS IS A PUZZLE IN FRONT OF ME, THAT YOU HAVE BROUGHT INTO MY SPHERE OF INFLUENCE. PLEASE HELP ME MAKE SENSE OF IT."

· WE NEED TO BE IN COMMUNITY

CAN A DEMONIC PRESENCE ATTACH ITSELF TO AN OBJECT OR PLACE?

BIBLICALLY:

· In the Old Testament, buildings (*"Now if a man consecrates his house as holy to the LORD"* (Leviticus 27:14-16)) and objects (*"You shall consecrate them so they will be most holy, and whatever touches them will be holy"* (Exodus 30:29)) were sanctified and dedicated to the Lord.

· There are many examples in the Old Testament of tearing down high places: *"then you shall drive out all the inhabitants of the land from before you, and destroy all their figured stones, and destroy all their molten images and demolish all their high places"* (Numbers 33:52)

· *"Or again, how can anyone enter a strong man's house and carry off his possessions unless he first ties up the strong man? Then he can plunder his house."* (Matthew 12:29)

· *"God did extraordinary miracles through Paul, so that even handkerchiefs and aprons that had touched him were taken to the sick, and their illnesses were cured and the evil spirits left them."* (Acts 19:11-12)

· Objects used in the worship of other gods needed to be destroyed - *"And a number of those who had practiced magic arts brought their books and burned them in front of everyone."* (Acts 19:19)

WHAT THIS LOOKS LIKE IN PRACTICE

· Anything used in worship to other gods

· Objects dedicated to another god

· Items bought in places where other religions are practiced, which might have been dedicated to other religions

· Freemasonry items you might inherit

· Items of clothing that celebrate the demonic

THE DEMONIC IN PLACES

· Places where other things or gods have been worshipped

· Places where enemy activity has gone on

· Places where you sense something 'isn't right'

HOW DO WE 'DELIVER' A PLACE OR OBJECT FROM ENEMY ACTIVITY?

In Nehemiah there's a process of repentance and dedication

· In chapter 1, Nehemiah discerns the sin of Israel that has led to their exile, and confesses the sins of the Israelites.

· In chapter 9 the Israelites confess their own sins plus the sins of their ancestors, recommit to God, and they worship.

· Then in chapter 12 the priests purify the people and reconsecrate the building and the city.

THE TOOLS WE USE ARE:

1. DISCERN

2. REPENT

3. OBJECTS

Ask God to highlight any things that give the enemy a foothold

4. REMOVE

5. CLEANSE

6. CONSECRATE (AND REDEDICATE)

7. WORSHIP

8. CHECKLIST

Go back to the list from the week on Spiritual Warfare and ask the Lord if you need to do any of those things

HOMEWORK

1. Ask the Lord for something, or someone, to pray over, to bring release from the enemy's oppression, e.g. your home, a thing in your home, a community place.

What do you need to pray out?

And what do you need to pray in?

2. If you want to go further in this topic, here are a couple of recommendations:

> · Derek Prince, *They Shall Expel Demons*
>
> · Charles Kraft, *Defeating Dark Angels*
>
> · Don Dickerman, *When Pigs Move In*

FURTHER DISCUSSION

We encourage you as a group to continue to process this content, along with other questions that you might have.

To help the conversation, here are a few stimulus questions:

1. Why do you think faith is the thing that amazes Jesus? Why is faith so important to Him?

2. Give yourself a score between 1 and 5 (1 is low, 5 is high) as to how full of faith you are in general, and then specifically when it comes to healing.

   Circle your answer.

   | 1 | 2 | 3 | 4 | 5 |

3. How can you raise your own level of faith? How can you help raise the level of faith in others?

4. Think of a situation when you would be bold enough to step out and pray for healing. What does it look like? What would you say?

5. What would you say to the person if the healing comes? What would you say or do if the healing doesn't happen?

6. What other questions do you have about healing?

MODULE B3:

How to Discern and Drive Out Demons

SESSION 2:

SIMPLE STEPS TO MINISTER DELIVERANCE

HOMEWORK REVIEW

What insights or questions come up as a result of asking the Lord to open your eyes to the work of the enemy?

Did you pray for anything/anyone to be released from the oppression of the enemy? If so, what happened?

CAN CHRISTIANS BE DEMONIZED?

"Do not give the devil a foothold" (Ephesians 4:27)

Peter in Mark 8: *"Get behind me, Satan"*

What if someone isn't saved but is open to deliverance?

> » Step one for anyone who isn't a Christian is to wholeheartedly put their faith in Jesus as their Savior and Lord.

> » Step two is to be filled with the Holy Spirit.

> » Step three is to cast our any demons.

5 LEVELS OF DEMONIC INFLUENCE

1. TEMPTATION

2. HARASSMENT

Flies (Beelzebub)

3. OPPRESSION

Attack like a band around your head

4. HABITATION

Demonized — it's there & has influence

5. POSSESSION

Not Christians (ownership)

The condition of our heart allows spirits to manifest — whether God's Holy Spirit or evil spirits.

HOW DO DEMONS ENTER?

1. WORDS

2. AGREEMENT

3. UNFORGIVENESS

4. ACTIONS

5. TRAUMA

6. PEOPLE

7. GENERATIONAL CURSES

8. DRUG ABUSE

9. SEXUAL IMMORALITY

10. OTHER RELIGIONS

Don't assume a one-size fits all response.

> » We must minister out of the leading of the Holy Spirit, not out of a preset formula.

OUR POSTURE

"From the Lord comes deliverance." (Psalm 3:8)

"And these signs will accompany those who believe: in my name they will cast out demons." (Mark 16:17)

1. AUTHORITY

"When Jesus had called the Twelve together, he gave them power and authority to drive out all demons and to cure diseases." (Luke 9:1)

2. SPIRIT EMPOWERED

3. SPIRITUAL GIFT

"...to another miraculous powers" (1 Corinthians 12:10)

4. DON'T GO LOOKING

5. DISCERNMENT

6. PAUSE

7. BY INVITATION

8. SECURITY

9. GLORIFY JESUS

PROCESSING TIME

1. You heard some examples of how demons might enter a person. Have you ever seen any of these in the lives of others (or yourself)?

2. As you look at the 'Our Posture' list, which do you do well, and where do you struggle / not have much experience?

In your room, whether in 2s or 3s, or as a whole group, take a few minutes to share some of your responses.

SIMPLE MODEL

1. Ask if you can pray for them, particularly for Jesus to come and to drive out any darkness or presence of the enemy that might be causing this issue.

2. As you begin to pray, welcome the presence of the Holy Spirit and perhaps say a word or two of honor to Jesus.

3. Then pause for 15-30 seconds and wait on Jesus to see what direction He might give for prayer (e.g. a cause, or how to pray, or a word of encouragement).

4. Command anything from the enemy to leave in Jesus' name. Be specific.

5. Ask the person how they're doing and if they felt or discerned anything. You might need to pray a little more in light of that.

6. Bless and fill that person with the Holy Spirit and ask Jesus to seal the good work that He has done in that moment.

SELF-ASSESSMENT

As you consider this simple model for ministering basic deliverance, how confident would you be to step into this role?

Give yourself a score between 1 and 5, where 1 = No way!, and 5 = I'm willing to do this, as the Spirit leads.

In your room, whether in 2s or 3s, or as a whole group, take a few minutes to share some of your responses.

SUBSTANTIAL MODEL

For times when a longer, more planned out and prepared time of ministry is the best way forward.

This is not meant to be spooky, intimidating or only for the super-anointed Christian!

By bringing it into the light, we can keep the enemy in perspective.

We can also feel a godly confidence that Jesus can use us, as part of a team, to unlock deliverance from the attacks of the enemy for anyone who truly seeks it.

PREPARATION

1. Have prayer back up and possibly fast in advance

2. Have the person being ministered to ask some of their mature Christian friends to pray

3. Never do it alone

4. Have some tissues to hand and a bin just in case throwing up occurs

5. Have anointing oil, a cross, communion, holy water or similar to hand

6. Have worship music to play in the background

DURING

1. Rely On the Holy Spirit

2. Honor the Individual

3. You're In Charge,

4. Relax

5. Begin With the Person

6. Glorify Jesus

7. Identify the Root Cause

8. Responsibility

9. Speak Out Loud

10. Command Prayer

11. Identify Legal Rights

12. Check In

13. Groups of Demons

14. Pace

15. Physical Symbols

Things You Can Say

Speak out loud with authority. Make declarations. Don't be timid. Short, punchy statements are often the best. Remember: the enemy is empowered through agreement with a lie.

- (to the person) We think there may well be some enemy activity going on here. Does that ring true with you?

  Would it be okay with you if we have a poke around and see?! You can interrupt at any time.

  Let us know what you sense is going on.

- Spirit of [fear] [*or whatever it is*], be gone in the name of Jesus!

- We declare that the enemy has no hold over this person because they are covered by the blood of Jesus.

- We rebuke the spirit of anxiety and break off any and all strongholds that you have gained in [Robin's] life. We command you to come out of [Robin] right now, without struggle, and we send you to the foot of the cross.

- We break off all and any curses in Jesus' name.

- Ask the person to pray, "In the name of Jesus, I revoke the generational curse of [fear] over my family. I renounce all of the sins of my ancestors that have led to this, or any other curses or sins in my life. I break any agreement with this curse. I proclaim that it will no longer affect me or my descendents."

- We bind any work of the enemy in the name of Jesus! He has no power or permission to do anything.

· We declare and release the freedom of Jesus over [Robin] right now.

· Holy Spirit, come! Come and fill this person completely.

AT THE END

1. FILL

2. REASSURE

3. DESTINY

4. PUSHBACK

5. NEXT STEPS

6. TEAM CLEANSING

"Greater is He who is in you than he who is in the world." (1 John 4:4).

MENTAL HEALTH AND DELIVERANCE

Be aware that there can sometimes be confusion between the demonic and mental health issues, especially as there's often overlap in how they manifest. Tread carefully.

A few thoughts:

- Jesus wants to bring healing and wholeness to all aspects of our humanity - spiritual, physical, mental, emotional, and so on.

- Demonic oppression is distinct from mental health issues

- Mental health issues should be recognized as what they are, and must never be shamed.

· The best thing to do is to enter with humility, leaning strongly into the discernment that the Holy Spirit gives.

· If you're not sure whether a condition is caused by a mental health problem or a demon, pause and don't rush in. Seek to gain insight from someone with more knowledge and experience.

· Be aware that different cultures have different attitudes to mental health issues, so cultural norms can shape responses.

HOMEWORK

1. Take some time to fast and pray for greater spiritual authority. While you might not have a specific situation in mind, ask the Lord to prepare you for the battles that lie ahead, as you submit in a deeper way, and allow God's authority to increase in you.

   If you find yourself stepping more into this area of ministry, seek to rally some praying people behind you. Think now who you might approach.

2. These are the most common causes of enemy oppression:

   » Spoken words by yourself or others, e.g. "You'll never be good enough", "You're not very intelligent", "I will never…"

   » Agreement with lies from the enemy that create strongholds in us, e.g. fear, addictive behavior, there'll never be enough, etc.

   » Unforgiveness or bitterness towards others.

   Take some time with the Lord and ask Him whether the enemy has been given a foothold in your life because of any of these.

   » If something comes to mind, confess it as sin and fully repent. Receive the full forgiveness that Jesus has won for you - maybe read 1 John 1:9 over yourself.

   (If nothing comes to mind, that's great! Take time to thank Jesus for His prior work in your life.)

» Declare out loud that the enemy no longer has any hold over you in this area.

» If you sense any lingering spirits, tell them to leave, e.g. "Any spirit of fear about lack of provision or similar, leave in the name of Jesus."

» Pray in the opposite (e.g. "Jesus, please fill me with a deep confidence that You are my faithful Provider!").

» You might want to ask God for a Bible verse to declare over yourself in the days ahead (it's fine to do a web search for a list of options from which to pick!)

FURTHER DISCUSSION

We encourage you as a group to continue to process this content, along with other questions that you might have.

To help the conversation, here are a few stimulus questions:

1. Why do you think faith is the thing that amazes Jesus? Why is faith so important to Him?

2. Give yourself a score between 1 and 5 (1 is low, 5 is high) as to how full of faith you are in general, and then specifically when it comes to healing.

3. How can you raise your own level of faith? How can you help raise the level of faith in others?

4. Think of a situation when you would be bold enough to step out and pray for healing. What does it look like? What would you say?

5. What would you say to the person if the healing comes? What would you say or do if the healing doesn't happen?

6. What other questions do you have about healing?

Moving Forward

FURTHER READING

Over the years we have read many books on growing in the naturally supernatural. Our aim here is to give you a list that is not overwhelming, yet has a good mixture of books to help you develop in this area. We have not included books that are out of print or hard to source in the United States.

These are in author alphabetical order, and with a comment or two to introduce each book to you.

Ruth Haley Barton, *Invitation to Solitude and Silence* (2004) — One woman's journey into the necessity of regular times of withdrawing to be with Jesus. Each chapter ends with a practice or exercise to try out, which gives the book a healthy focus on application.

Mike Bickle, *Growing in the Prophetic* (1995) — From someone who pastored a church with a prominent and yet at times chaotic prophetic ministry, those lessons learned create an insightful and practical resource.

Christoph Blumhardt, *The Gospel of God's Reign* (2014) — 19th Century German theologian, also a prominent evangelist, faith healer, and politician, his writings focus on bringing God's Kingdom around us by all means possible. Stimulating, even if you don't agree with everything he says!

Shawn Bolz, *God Secrets* (2017) — Engaging teaching on developing the gift of words of knowledge, including content on what to do when you get it wrong. Shawn Bolz has a very public track record of operating in this gift, and does a good job demystifying its usage.

Michael Cassidy, *Bursting the Wineskins* (1983) — Written from an African perspective by the man who is the Honorary Chair of the Lausanne Movement, Michael uses his story as a framework to teach Biblically about entering into life in the Spirit.

Dave Clayton, *Revival Starts Here: A Short Conversation on Prayer, Fasting and Revival for Beginners Like Me* (2018) — Practical and non-guilt inducing challenge to step more into fasting and prayer, with lots of application ideas. A great short read!

Jack Deere, *Surprised by the Power of the Spirit* (1993) — The inspiring story of how a cessationist seminary professor had his life and ministry turned upside down as he experienced the power and presence of the Holy Spirit.

Don Dickerman, *When Pigs Move In* (2009) — A very practical book on deliverance, that contains a host of testimonies, followed by lots of details on the nuts and bolts of this vital ministry, all in an easy-to-read style.

James Dunn, *Jesus and the Spirit* (1975) — One of the defining scholarly works on the work of the Spirit, this is very readable and engaging. It does an excellent job of unpacking the Spirit experiences of Jesus and the Early Church. (Dunn was also Alex's NT professor at university!)

Gordon Fee, *God's Empowering Presence* (1994) — Fee was one of the first Pentecostals to earn a PhD in Biblical studies, and he combines the two streams in this book by literally exegeting every reference to the Spirit in Paul's writings - but the result is anything but a dry academic read.

Michael Green, *Evangelism in the Early Church* (1970) — A fascinating read, with all sorts of nuggets that reveal how the Early Church was so effective in reaching others with Gospel. This includes being a Spirit-filled people, and the use of the gifts is well recorded.

Bill Johnson, *God is Good* (2016) — An uplifting read about trusting in the goodness of God as revealed in Scripture, so that we in turn can reveal His goodness in the power of the Spirit to a broken world.

Bill Johnson & Randy Clark, *The Essential Guide to Healing* (2011) — An excellent book on how to heal the sick, with practical teaching, stirring stories, and sensible wisdom for developing this ministry in a church context.

Charles Kraft, *Defeating Dark Angels* (2016) — Clear, Biblically grounded teaching on how demonic oppression takes place, and how to minister deliverance. Kraft has many books, and we found this one to be very helpful and practical.

George Eldon Ladd, *The Gospel of the Kingdom* (1959) — A hugely influential book, which explores the mystery that the Kingdom of God is both now and simultaneously not yet, and how the Spirit empowers us to go out on mission to extend God's kingly rule.

George Eldon Ladd, *The Presence of the Future* (1974) — The big idea in this book is that the breaking in of the present, dynamic rule of God is the central concept behind Jesus' message and mission - and thus should be for ours.

Francis MacNutt, *Healing* **(1974, although look for the updated version)** — This was the first modern-era book on healing that has (deservedly) been widely read, and you can see its influence still today. Very practical and packed full of nuggets of wisdom.

Charles Price, *The Real Faith* **(1930s)** — After experiencing baptism in the Spirit in the 1920s, his ministry was transformed and saw incredible healings. This short book is the best reflection on the nature of faith and the naturally supernatural life that we have found.

Derek Prince, *They Shall Expel Demons* **(1998)** — Prince wrote numerous books on deliverance, and this is an excellent primer into this area. Sensible, Biblical, faith-filled, it contains wise teaching and helpful stories gained from many years of experience.

David Pytches, *Come Holy Spirit* **(1994)** — Written more like a logical, list-driven, logistical handbook, this was such a help in our early years of ministering in the power of the Spirit, as it gives you all the major points in a systematic way.

Jon Ruthven, *On the Cessation of the Charismata: The Protestant Polemic on Post-biblical Miracles* **(1993)** — A brilliant deconstruction of cessationism, written from a scholarly Biblical perspective, full of close exegesis of texts and clear arguments.

Jordan Seng, *Miracle Work* **(2012)** — A great overview of ministering in the spiritual gifts, with each teaching chapter followed by a short story chapter, which makes it all feel very grounded and attainable.

Sam Storms, *Practicing the Power* **(2017)** — This book does a great job of showing how stepping into the spiritual gifts is deeply rooted in Scripture. It's especially useful for those who come from a Reformed Calvinist perspective, which is the author's background.

Jerry Trousdale, *Miraculous Movements: How Hundreds of Thousands of Muslims Are Falling in Love with Jesus* **(2012)** — We both love this book! It is packed full of inspirational stories of how the church is growing globally AND gives tools that we can use here in the West.

Jerry Trousdale & Glenn Sunshine, *The Kingdom Unleashed* **(2018)** — Revealing insights on how the church in the Global South is growing rapidly through Disciple-Making Movements. Lots of takeaways on living the principles of Acts today.

Kris Vallotton, *Basic Training for the Prophetic Ministry* (2014) — A down-to-earth, clear and helpful training in the prophetic gifts, which feels as if a very fatherly member of your church is steering you into greater maturity!

Mark & Pam Virkler, *How to Hear God's Voice* (2005) — Designed more as a workbook (with lots of note taking space), it contains Biblical teaching and helpful exercises, and in particular a focus on encountering God through waiting on Him.

David & Paul Watson, *Contagious Disciple Making* (2014) — Learning from Disciple-Making Movements across the globe, the stories here are fabulous, and there is much content on how to make disciples in a naturally supernatural way.

Dallas Willard, *The Divine Conspiracy* (1998) — An engaging and thoughtful study about the nature of the Gospel of the Kingdom that Jesus preaches - which is not a set of rules to follow, but a declaration of God's active rule and His invitation for us to enter in and partner with Him.

John Wimber & Kevin Springer, *Power Evangelism* (1985) — Explains Jesus' theology of the Kingdom, and then moves to show how this transforms our evangelism, with lots of practical stories and ideas for taking your next step.

John Wimber & Kevin Springer, *Power Healing* (1987) — A classic text that has influenced many leaders. It creates a Biblical theology of healing, based on how Jesus operated, and then applies those principles with wisdom and experience.

Brother Yun, *The Heavenly Man* (2002) — An inspirational first-hand account from Chinese house church leader Brother Yun, who has led a huge movement in the power of the Spirit in the face of severe persecution. Some amazing stories!

NEXT STEPS

YOUR NEXT PART OF THE NATURALLY SUPERNATURAL COURSE

Congratulations on completing the Foundations part of The Naturally Supernatural Course! We hope that you have been strengthened in your awareness of the Father's love, deepened in your commitment to Jesus, and equipped to grow in a Spirit-empowered lifestyle.

The next part of The Naturally Supernatural Course is **Part C: Expansion**. As in this book, there are 3 modules there, covering the following topics:

Module C1: Words of Knowledge and Words of Wisdom

- Session 1 — God's 'Now' Words of Life

- Session 2 — How to Grow in Spiritual Hearing

Module C2: Growing in Healing

- Session 1 — Developing the Heart of a Healer

- Session 2 — Emotional Healing

Module C3: The Gifts of Miracles and Faith

- Session 1 — Miracles and Everyday Life

- Session 2 — Growing the Muscles of Faith

Those are some fascinating, important, but often misunderstood (and sometimes misused) topics! You will look at them through extensive engagement with many of the relevant Scriptures, real-life stories, practical exercises, and lots of room for dialogue, processing, and personal application.

To buy access to this material, go to *naturallysupernaturalcourse.com* and follow the link to Part C: Expansion. As you've already discovered, the relevant Course Book can be purchased and shipped to you from Amazon.

ACCOMPANYING BOOKS

Over the next few years, our plan is to write a book to accompany each of the 12 modules covered in this Course. That format will allow us to include more material than is sometimes possible in these videos, while also giving a written reference guide for you to quickly access.

The first few books are already published at the time of recording the videos, with several more in the pipeline! As time goes on more will be released. You can find the books in paperback and ebook formats on Amazon.

If you would like to know whenever a new book is released, either 'follow' us as authors on Amazon (they will then email you as new books are published), or sign up for our ministry emails at *dandelionresourcing.com*.

ACCESS MORE RESOURCES

As a couple our call from God is to equip the wider church with practical tools like this book. To help facilitate this, we lead the team at Dandelion Resourcing.

As Dandelion we focus on three core areas:

- Being naturally supernatural
- Disciple-making
- Living on mission

We find that when all three of those circles of life overlap, a Kingdom culture is formed that leads to dynamic life, impact, and growth.

To help ground this into practice, and with passionate believers like you in mind, we have developed a range of resources:

FREE CONTENT

We regularly produce free short videos and articles. The focus is on our three core areas - being naturally supernatural, disciple-making, and living on mission.

If you drop your name and email in the sign-up box on dandelionresourcing. com, we'll send you an email each time a new video is released. You'll also hear about other resources and training opportunities that we develop over time. (And you can one-click unsubscribe at any time!)

NATURALLY SUPERNATURAL COACHING COHORT

The material in this Course was first taught and developed in our online small group cohorts. Aimed at Kingdom leaders, this is a 12 month process that meets as a group of 6-10 screens online twice a month.

If you are interested in finding out more, please go to *dandelionresourcing.com/ naturally-supernatural-cohort*.

BRING US TO YOUR CONFERENCE AND CHURCH

We have found that coming in person to a church or conference allows for a great depth of impact, transformation, and equipping in your local context. It's also a lot of fun to be together! Faith rises in the hearts of those who attend, by God's grace the Holy Spirit ministers, and there is a catalytic move forward.

Our heart is to resource disciples to make more disciples, so everything we do is about multiplication. Thus over a few days together, you'll likely see a whole lot of people given fresh boldness to step into the things of the Spirit. It's not about the speakers, it's about the body of Christ being equipped and empowered to go!

If you're interested in having one or both of us come in, please contact us via our ministry website, dandelionresourcing.com. While we only spend a small amount of time traveling, we do prayerfully consider every invitation.

COULD YOU HELP US OUT?

If you have enjoyed this book and course, please could you do us a quick favor?

The best way for others to find out about a resource like this is through personal recommendation (think about what makes you investigate a new book). With that in mind, we would be so honored **if you would take a moment to share a quick review with others**.

The #1 place is on Amazon — pop in your stars and write a comment, and that will help us enormously. (As you no doubt know, the more reviews, the more their algorithms will highlight this book - and thus the course — to others.)

In addition, please do share about this book (post a photo of you and your group holding the cover!) on social media — feel free to tag us in the shot!

Thank you so much in advance.

Again, thank you for reading — we're praying that you have so much Jesus-honoring fruitfulness as you step further into a naturally supernatural lifestyle.

With love and blessings,

Alex and Hannah

ACKNOWLEDGEMENTS

Over the years so many people have helped us grow into a naturally supernatural lifestyle. Some have been leaders, others friends, and yet others would never know our names or faces, but have shaped us through their teachings, books, podcasts, and lives.

However, a number of specific people have intentionally helped us with this book - and we are thankful for each one of them:

- Caity Shinnick designed the cover and did all the internal layout work, which turned our chicken scratch into something lovely to look at.

- Darren Galindo is our videographer, and did a wonderful job of filming and editing the accompanying videos.

- The Garden Church in Long Beach CA, who generously invested into this project and gave us space to film.

- Generous friends and donors who have supported us financially, which gives us room to write, create, plan, film, edit, and produce this material.

- Our Naturally Supernatural Coaching Cohorts, where we together worked through a lot of this material in its early forms. Your questions, stories, comments, and insights have hugely helped us hone and develop this teaching material. Obviously now any errors or mistakes in the Naturally Supernatural Course are entirely the fault of you lot and nothing to do with us!!

- Finally, to our children, we love doing this stuff with you!

ABOUT THE AUTHORS

Alex and Hannah Absalom lead Dandelion Resourcing, which empowers Christians to go and form disciple-making disciples of Jesus in naturally super-natural ways. Originally from England, they have been in church leadership since 1994, live in Long Beach CA, and with their three young adult sons are missionaries to the USA.

 dandelionresourcing.com

f facebook.com/dandelionresourcing

[O] instagram.com/alexabsalom

🐦 twitter.com/alexabsalom

Made in the USA
Columbia, SC
18 April 2023

15547026R00087